Communication Skills

TALK YOURSELF INTO A JOB

Chris Webb

M

First edition 1978
Reprinted (first Papermac edition) 1979

Published by
THE MACMILLAN PRESS LTD
London and Basingstoke
Associated companies in Delhi Dublin
Hong Kong Johannesburg Lagos Melbourne
New York Singapore and Tokyo

Printed in Great Britain by
A. Wheaton & Co., Ltd., Exeter

British Library Cataloguing in Publication Data

Webb, Chris
    Communication skills.
    1. Applications for positions
    I Title
    331.1.28   HF5383

ISBN 0-333-22362-4

CONTENTS

The Main Sections:

The Skills of Self-Appraisal

The Skills of Making Contact

The Skills of Meeting People

EDITOR'S NOTE

This workbook in Communication is, like its forerunner "Communication in Practice", intended for young people in their last year of compulsory schooling or early years as college students. Whilst it is generally recognised that appropriate academic qualifications are very useful, if not always essential, in seeking employment or for settling down happily in it, it is not always remembered or understood that there are other aspects of these processes which are equally important. This book deals with these "additional" matters in a way which will, we think, confirm that they are indeed essential elements in becoming a mature person. We know you can build on this foundation and will enjoy using the book.

Henley College of Further Education,
Coventry

HARRY SPENCE
General Editor

ACKNOWLEDGEMENT

To Caroline Eaves and Ann Webb for assistance in presentation and layout.

INTRODUCTION

This is a workbook for developing your communication skills and helping your personal development. But personal development is a very big subject. It could cover anything from building up your biceps to buying a new suit. This book is centred on one aspect of your personal development,

GETTING A JOB

It aims to concentrate on the skills you need when you apply for a job. This does not mean it is only aimed at people who do not have jobs. If you are already in employment this book should help you in your career progress. If you have not yet started work this book may help to secure the RIGHT JOB for you. Either way, working through the exercises will develop your skills in the use of language.

Let's begin with the question of the RIGHT JOB.

Your work is vital to you: it defines your life. One of the first questions we ever ask about someone is, "What does he do for a living?"

It is very important that the job you do is one you like. If you are keen and enthusiastic about your job you are more likely to be successful in it, and what is more, feel happy and contented. To try to ensure that we really like the job we choose, it may be helpful to ask ourselves one or two questions. Effective communication begins when we start to know ourselves.

NOTE

IN THIS BOOK   ■   MEANS SOMETHING TO DO

●   MEANS SOMETHING TO REMEMBER

THE SKILLS OF
SELF-APPRAISAL

1. TAKE A LOOK AT YOURSELF.

It is natural for most of us to seek out the company of others. There are people who enjoy being alone, but usually this is for short periods. The idea of being completely cut off from everyone else is very frightening to most people.

Make a list of all the different groups to which you belong, e.g. family
1.
2.
3.
4.
5.
6.
7.
8.

Many of the people you know, you will have met as part of a group. Perhaps you sit with the same group of people at lunch every day. Maybe you go to the same club every Saturday.

This kind of social life is vital to all of us.

There are lessons in this for anyone interested in people. Being a member of a group is natural to us. It is part of our humanity. Experts believe that people first formed into groups to survive.

A solitary Stone Age man would have been easy prey for a leopard or a sabre-toothed tiger. Collectively, men had more chance of survival.

■ Man is a GREGARIOUS animal.
Write down the dictionary definition of GREGARIOUS. List six other GREGARIOUS animals. Why do you think they are gregarious?

Definition:

1.	4.
2.	5.
3.	6.

Centuries ago the poet John Donne wrote, "No man is an island." By this he meant that we all need other people.

● 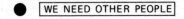 WE NEED OTHER PEOPLE

People do not form into groups by accident. Whichever society scholars study they note the tendency for people to meet and act collectively. It is therefore logical to assume that people come together because they NEED one another.

We need different groups for different things. In our lives different people will serve different purposes.

> Refer to the first exercise and list again the groups to which you belong. Now write against them what you consider is the main purpose of the group for you.
>
> | Group | Purpose |
> |---|---|
> | e.g. family | security |
>
> 1.
>
> 2.
>
> 3.
>
> 4.
>
> 5.
>
> 6.
>
> 7.
>
> 8.

● GROUPS SATISFY NEEDS

8

Unless you are very unusual you have probably begun to find that there are two main types of group in your life. Some groups meet because people want them to meet. Individuals like one another's company, they share a common interest, they enjoy meeting together. These groups are part of a person's social life and are usually defined as, INFORMAL.

The other kind of group is associated with work. It usually meets because it has a job to do. People join the group to perform a particular task, for example, a class in a school, a group of typists, a board of directors. This kind of group is usually called FORMAL.

■ List the groups you belong to under FORMAL and INFORMAL headings.

	FORMAL	INFORMAL
1.		
2.		
3.		
4.		

● THERE ARE GROUPS FOR WORK AND GROUPS FOR PLAY

In an ideal job, of course, you would meet people to do your work, but you would also enjoy the work activity and the company of people around you.

In terms of getting to know ourselves however it is probably the INFORMAL GROUPS which are most revealing. There is an old proverb which says, "Judge a man by his friends, he can't help his relatives."

IF WE ACCEPT THE IDEA THAT GROUPS CAN SATISFY OUR NEEDS, THEN BY EXAMINING THE GROUPS TO WHICH WE BELONG WE MAY BE ABLE TO FIND OUT SOME OF THE THINGS WHICH MAKE US TICK.

List the groups you belong to in descending order according to how much you enjoy being part of them.

1. (most enjoyable)

2.

3.

4.

5.

6.

7.

8. (least enjoyable)

People who study such matters — social psychologists — might suggest that our enjoyment in being part of a group depends upon whether the group satisfies our needs.

If you are a member of a football team it is probably an important part of your social life. If you are doing well and receiving praise from your friends you will enjoy your soccer. If things are going badly for you and criticism is coming your way you will probably begin to feel that you no longer really belong to the team.

This feeling of belonging to a group is sometimes called AFFILIATION. If we identify strongly with a group our affiliation is said to be high. If we feel we do not really belong to the group our affiliation is said to be low.

> Write down the group to which you feel you have the highest affiliation. Give reasons why you feel you belong to it.
>
> Group
>
> Reason
>
> ---
>
> Now state the group to which you have the lowest affiliation. Why do you think this is?
>
> Group
>
> Reason

The reasons you have given for feeling part of a group will depend upon your personality.

 DIFFERENT PEOPLE HAVE DIFFERENT NEEDS

One expert has argued that there are FIVE types of need in people.

1. SURVIVAL NEEDS — the need for basics like food, water and air

2. SECURITY NEEDS — the need for safety

3. SOCIAL NEEDS — the need to belong, to feel accepted

4. EGO NEEDS — the need to gain respect from others, to have influence

5. CREATIVE NEEDS — the need to fulfil oneself, to create something

Given that the vast majority of people in our country today have the first two needs satisfied, it is probably a combination of the last three needs which affects our affiliation to a group.

List the groups you belong to according to which you think they mainly satisfy.		
SOCIAL needs	EGO needs	CREATIVE needs

The analysis you have just done should reveal something about your own personal needs. If most of your groups are listed under the EGO heading this could suggest that these needs are strongest in you, and the same could, of course, apply to the other categories.

DIFFERENT GROUPS SATISFY DIFFERENT NEEDS

Many people assume that a job is only about money. They argue that the only satisfaction in a job is the pay packet at the end of the week. But the whole point of our work on groups is to show that there should be more to a job than money because our working

life is as much about needs being satisfied as is our social life. Human beings need more from life than just survival. A job should satisfy all our needs if it is to involve us fully.

When you think about the percentage of waking hours spent at work it should

become obvious that to be fully satisfied in a job you need to be interested in it and feel that you belong amongst your workmates.

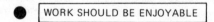

WORK SHOULD BE ENJOYABLE

But to be contented at work you should have a clear idea of what you want to get out of a job. It should be a job which will give you a chance to satisfy all of your needs, not just provide you with money.

> Say how the job you have chosen (or are thinking about) satisfies the following three needs (if, of course, you think it does).
>
> SOCIAL
>
> EGO
>
> CREATIVE
>
> What is the most important need for you? Why?

CHOOSE A JOB WHICH PROMISES TO INVOLVE YOU

TAKE A LOOK AT YOURSELF

THINGS TO TRY

■ A   Write an essay on any of the following:—

My ideal job
How I see myself in ten years' time
Job satisfaction

■ B   Describe yourself as seen by:—

1. your father
2. someone who teaches you
3. your best friend
4. someone meeting you for the first time at interview

■ C   Give an account of any occasion when you have felt loyalty to someone. What is loyalty? Why did you feel it?

■ D   Have you been part of any group, at school, college, work or outside, which has broken up? Try to describe why it broke up.

■ E   Imagine you have been put in charge of a small group of people. Design a slogan — maximum ten words — to remind your group that it is important to cooperate and work together.

■ F   Imagine you are giving a reference for yourself. Write comments about your personality, character, abilities, aptitudes, etc. for a prospective employer.

THE SKILLS OF SELF-APPRAISAL

WHAT YOU HAVE LEARNED

CHAPTER 1 – TAKE A LOOK AT YOURSELF

● WE NEED OTHER PEOPLE

● GROUPS SATISFY NEEDS

● THERE ARE GROUPS FOR WORK AND GROUPS FOR PLAY

● DIFFERENT PEOPLE HAVE DIFFERENT NEEDS

● DIFFERENT GROUPS SATISFY DIFFERENT NEEDS

● WORK SHOULD BE ENJOYABLE

● CHOOSE A JOB WHICH PROMISES TO INVOLVE YOU

THE SKILLS OF
MAKING CONTACT

2. READING FOR FACTS.

The obvious way to get to know about jobs and careers is through Careers Teachers and Career Offices. Additionally you may know someone who is already doing the job you are considering. It is good sense to have a chat with him about what is entailed in the work. Of course you must get all the help you can, but there are ways you can supplement advice by using and developing your own skills. The first contact you are likely to have with any prospective employer is through the Press.

■

What is a Trade Publication? Write down a definition. List some Trade Publications connected with your chosen career.
Definition:
1.
2.
3.
4.

Careful reading is a very important skill. The more you develop it the more you are likely to come to sound decisions based on facts.

● KNOWLEDGE COMES FROM READING

The only reliable way to improve your skill with words is to read widely. Whatever job you choose this is an important skill in giving you access to the promotion ladder.

Questions	Your Answer
1. How many words do you think there are in the English Language?	
2. How many words does the average person understand?	
3. How many different words does the average person use in a week?	

Answers

1. There are approximately half a million words in the Complete Oxford English Dictionary.

2. Scholars estimate the average person understands about ten thousand words.

3. It is estimated that on average we use about seven hundred words per week (counting a word like "the" as only one word, however many times it is used).

YOU CAN ALWAYS EXTEND YOUR VOCABULARY

Here are some important words connected with jobs. Define their meaning with the help of a dictionary.

	Definition
1. Career	
2. Attitude	
3. Motivation	
4. Achievement	
5. Intelligence	
6. Aptitude	
7. Disposition	
8. Circumstances	

IF YOU DON'T UNDERSTAND A WORD LOOK IT UP

It is very possible that your first contact with a job will be through a newspaper or magazine advertisement. This is an area where careful reading is extremely important. Advertisements generally can be misleading, unless we use our judgement properly.

Read this house advertisement. Re-write it giving a
purely factual version of the house being advertised.
What important facts are omitted?

You're gonna love this gem — it's a steal at the price.
Period style, bijou cottage residence, all oak beams
and lattice windows. Hostess hall with snug, inviting
cloakroom calculated to impress all those guests
you'll just have to invite to your new pad.

Film star lounge overlooking easily managed gardens.
Attractive dining recess leading on to dream kitchen.
After this you float up the curved staircase to three
luxurious bedrooms and a breath-taking bathroom.
You'll have to see it to believe it, but don't wait too
long — this one will go in days.

Of course, the fact that advertisements can be misleading does not mean that the
intention is to deceive. The writer of the advertisement may be trying, quite
legitimately, to stress the favourable aspects of what he is trying to sell. He must
also, of course, be honest to observe the Trades Descriptions Act.

Alternatively an advertisement may be vague because advertising is expensive and a firm may cut its costs by reducing the number of words.

■

> Read the following three advertisements for jobs. What is the main quality you think the firms are looking for in the successful applicant?
>
> ---
>
> A fabulous opening for
> with-it school leaver.
> Opportunities for travel.
> Irregular hours.
> Box 61.
>
> ---
>
> Fed-up? Bored?
> Looking for Promotion?
> Want the challenge of
> management? Contact
> Cutler's of Cape Street
> to change your life.
>
> ---
>
> Intelligent young person
> of smart appearance for
> clerical work in solicitor's
> office. Phone 32614.

● TRY TO READ BETWEEN THE LINES

Most people read mainly for pleasure. Newspapers, magazines, novels all provide enjoyable ways of passing the time. But this kind of reading is different from reading to obtain facts.

HISTORICAL
NOVELS

24

To ensure we get the facts from what we read we should MAKE NOTES. If we are reading an advertisement for a job we should note the relevant facts, for example the name of the company and its address. If reading is necessary to give you background information about a job it is important you make notes on the content, otherwise it is very likely that you will forget everything you have read.

Make a note of the three most important facts in the following advertisement.

Wanted: For progressive company in fast-moving business. Young person with management potential. Should be self-starter and good organiser. Good speech and appearance vital. Must be willing to work irregular hours. Fantastic prospects for right applicant. Tel. 46234. Business hours only.

1.

2.

3.

MAKE NOTES TO REMEMBER FACTS

As well as the limited number of words in advertisements there is another source of potential confusion. Once again, in order to cut costs, advertisers quite often use abbreviations and jargon.

■

Write down the dictionary definition of "jargon".
Then write in the space provided the meaning of the
following abbreviations and jargon phrases used in
job advertisements. If you do not understand any
find out what they mean.

Definition of JARGON

appship.	
bckgd.	
dept.	
co.	
asst.	
trnee.	
agcy.	
ext.	
ltd.	
L.V.s	
S.A.E.	
piecework	
shiftwork	
referees	
a week in hand	

● | LEARN IMPORTANT ABBREVIATIONS AND JARGON |

READING FOR FACTS

THINGS TO TRY

■ A   Write an essay on one of the following:—

Careers Guidance
The Usefulness of Libraries
The Local Press and the Community

■ B   Read through your favourite magazine.
List all the abbreviations used. Why do
you think they were preferred to the full
versions?

■ C   Take one "popular" newspaper and one
"quality" newspaper published on the same
day. Compare the way they treat the same
"stories". How does the vocabulary
compare? How do you account for the
difference?

■ D   Take a copy of a local newspaper and
select one job advertisement from it.
From the few clues it gives you try and
develop a fuller idea of the job. List the
main duties you think are involved and the
employer's requirements. What do you
judge are the prospects for training and
promotion? Is it a job for you?

■ E   What are the different sources of information
about jobs? List them and compare their
relative merits.

3. SPEAKING ON THE TELEPHONE.

When you are getting in touch with a company or organisation about a job it is very likely that you will have to contact them at some point by telephone. Many advertisements give telephone numbers instead of addresses. Often applicants must ask for application forms by telephoning someone at the company. Additionally you may have been late in seeing an advertisement and want to know if a job is still open. Using the telephone is a quick and convenient way of making contact. But BEWARE. Using a telephone properly is not as easy as some people assume.

It is quite different from speaking to someone face to face. When you can see your listener you have a great many clues which help you when you speak to him. His eyes can help you to gauge whether he is understanding what you are telling him. His facial expressions may reveal whether he is paying attention. These aids to communication are not available over the telephone.

Some people fail to realise this. It is quite usual to see people using gestures when they are speaking on the telephone. They have become so used to depending on their hands to help them explain things that they use them even when their listener cannot see them.

List the things you can see which help you to talk with someone face to face, e.g. eyes, facial expressions.
1.
2.
3.
4.
5.

I LOATHE YOU

HE LOVES ME

In conversations over the telephone your voice is on its own. In ordinary conversation you can use gestures like pointing to stress a point. In ordinary conversation you can see whether your listener understands you and then adapt accordingly. You have what some experts call instant FEEDBACK. Your listener can feed information back to you about whether he is following you. You will soon see if he is not.

This is not so over the telephone. Many misunderstandings arise because of telephone conversations. The most common problem is, of course, mishearing people. Unless your pronunciation is clear, it is very possible that your listener may get the wrong message from you.

SPEAK CLEARLY

■
> List some possible reasons why a Personnel
> Officer in a large company might mishear what
> a caller is saying to him over the telephone,
> e.g. noise in the office.

1.

2.

3.

4.

5.

6.

There is always a danger that messages which are important to you seem trivial to other people. It might be vital to you that you secure a job, but a clerk dealing with your query may have his mind on other things. It is often a good idea to create FEEDBACK by asking for messages to be read back. Equally it is wise to spell any unusual words, particularly in names and addresses.

■
> When you are using the telephone to leave a
> message, how can you ensure that it is
> accurately recorded?

Indicate the things which you consider could be improved in the following telephone conversation.

WHEN DEALING WITH FACTS BE PRECISE

Being polite is always a help, particularly over the telephone. Some scholars believe that language began as a kind of REASSURANCE. A mother talking to a baby, a wife to a husband, a nurse to a patient, all use language to reassure. Being polite is another form of reassurance. We are demonstrating consideration for others and in

so doing making a good impression. If you consider phrases like "Good Morning" or "How do you do?" you can soon see how we use words to reassure others. After all, these phrases have little or no meaning. We all say

"Good Morning" to others when the weather is dreadful. The phrase began as "I hope you are going to have a good morning" or some old-fashioned version of that sentence. It was a sign that one person cared about another. And it is only by being considerate to others that we can expect consideration in return.

> You are phoning a Mr. Jones, a Personnel Manager about a job. Write down the first two or three sentences you would say to him.

⬤ BE POLITE

As well as getting our approach right it is important that the mechanics of making a telephone call are understood, particularly if you need to use a public call box.

Imagine a friend has asked for some tips on using a call box telephone. What advice would you add to the list below to help him use the equipment properly?

1. Have a clear idea of what you want to say before phoning.

2. Keep and pencil and paper handy.

3. Spell out any difficult words in names and addresses.

4.

5.

6.

7.

8.

Many people who use the telephone regularly are not really familiar with the equipment. They blunder on, using the telephone day in and day out, without a thought. That may be acceptable if you are using the phone for unimportant matters, but if you are making a call connected with something as important as a job, then you need to get it right.

Describe briefly the sound you would hear when you get the following tones on the telephone.

1.   A dialling tone

2.   A ringing tone

3.   An engaged tone

4.   A pay tone (in a call box)

5.   A number unobtainable tone

6.   Crossed lines

1.

2.

3.

4.

5.

6.

LEARN TO OPERATE THE TELEPHONE

SPEAKING ON THE TELEPHONE

THINGS TO TRY

A   Write an essay on one of the following:—

Are accents an advantage or a disadvantage?
The impact of the telephone
Manners

B   Design a notice to be placed near a telephone to help people to use the telephone properly.

C   Imagine you are a salesman for the Post Office. How would you set about selling a telephone installation to the following people and institutions:—

1.   An ordinary family
2.   A country school
3.   A Student Union in a Technical College
4.   A Sixth-form Society in a School

D   You want to leave a message for a Personnel Officer you are trying to contact about a job. Describe how you would go about giving the message to his secretary.

E   Prepare a short talk on "The telephone — uses and abuses."

4. WRITING LETTERS.

In many ways the first part of the nineteenth century was the great age of letter writing. Before the development of modern transport systems and the invention of the telephone, the letter was the quickest and most effective way of communicating at a distance. As a result many of the "rules" of letter writing originated in the last century. "Rules" is really the wrong word, because no one can lay down strict procedures about something like letter writing. There are only the usual ways of doing it, called CONVENTIONS.

> Write down the Dictionary definition of "convention". Apart from letter writing conventions, name five other types of convention. What purposes do they serve?
>
> Definition:
>
> 1.
>
> 2.
>
> 3.
>
> 4.
>
> 5.

Some conventions are merely relics of the past. They continue only because people cannot be bothered to change them. Other conventions survive because they are useful. In letter writing we can find both kinds of convention.

The first type of convention — the one which is not useful, but harmful — affects the way people express themselves in letters. Many people still seem to believe that letters should be written in an old-fashioned kind of language. Perhaps this is the nineteenth century influence we mentioned before. Even today you will find some business letters contain out-of-date expressions like "I am in receipt of your esteemed favour" or "We should deem it a favour to call on the 15th instant."

Cherished and illustrious Sir,

It is important to remember that letter writing is not a separate form of English. You do not need to use a special kind of language to write letters.

■

> Write down simple alternatives to the following unnecessarily complicated or unfamiliar words and phrases.
>
> e.g. deem   consider

1. at this moment in time

2. all personnel

3. in the immediate vicinity

4. appertaining to

5. utilize

6. commence

7. a percentage of

8. regarding

9. customary channels

10. in receipt of

● ┌──────────────────────────────────────┐
  │ WRITE NATURALLY, DON'T BE POMPOUS │
  └──────────────────────────────────────┘

What you need to write letters is what you need to write anything — an EFFECTIVE STYLE.

There is a tendency nowadays to make the written word into a very formal means of expression. People are tempted to dress up simple statements to make them sound more important, particularly when they are trying to make a good impression through a letter. It is this tendency which can lead away from "calling a spade a spade" to calling a spade "A MANUALLY OPERATED EXCAVATING INSTRUMENT".

■

Reduce the following sentence to as few words as possible while preserving its meaning. You may alter any words you want to.

It is apparent that in the final and ultimate analysis a considerable proportion of time and a fair amount of effort could be saved by an overall and comprehensive improvement in operator and plant utilization.

● | WRITE SIMPLY |

In the event of a fire, proceed at once by the most direct route to the nearest exit point.

This pompous way of writing is not new. In some ways it is part of the fabric of our language. It is as old as the English Language — which in reality is not very old. Modern English, as we know it, began to emerge around the fourteenth century.

English is a mongrel language.

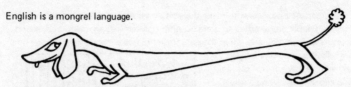

It was formed centuries ago by a combination of two main languages, Anglo-Saxon and Latin. Latin was brought here by the Normans when they invaded England in 1066. Their kind of Norman French was very close to the original Latin language. Anglo-Saxon was spoken by the people the Normans conquered.

As a result Anglo-Saxon words became associated with the conquered race and Latinate words with the ruling class. Gradually, by a process of association, people came to think that Anglo-Saxon words — which were usually short — were not as good as Latin words, which were usually long. When the two languages eventually fused to form Modern English the same prejudices lived on.

The Norman (Latinate) versions of "pig", "cow", "sheep", "calf" were pork, beef, mutton and veal (allowing for some changes in spelling). Why do you think we use the Latinate versions when we eat the meat?

People often seem to think that using long words is a sign of being educated.

But if we adopt a common sense approach to language we can soon see that using long words, for their own sake, can get us into trouble with our reader. If our aim is to communicate effectively, long words can get in the way, particularly in a letter. When we are speaking to someone face to face we can see them and judge whether they understand us or not. Letter writing is different. We cannot stand with the person reading our letter and explain every word to him. We often do not know who will be reading our letter and which words they can understand. The only way to ensure that everyone can understand

what we write is to choose FAMILIAR words wherever possible.

Study the words in List A and provide familiar alternatives in List B — e.g. (A) domicile (B) house.

Words of Latinate Origin	Words of Anglo-Saxon Origin
(A)	(B)
benevolent	
unilateral	
ameliorate	
adjacent	
facilitate	
commence	
purchase	
renovate	
constitute	
terminate	

● CHOOSE FAMILIAR WORDS WHENEVER POSSIBLE

In our approach to writing letters we must constantly consider the reader.
The guidelines we have so far established arise out of that consideration. They are
not an attempt to establish what is "correct English".

Many discussions about "correct English" are a waste of time because they are based
upon a misunderstanding of what language is. Language is a LIVING THING, a vital
part of life, society and culture. As such it is constantly subject to change and
modification. People who have rigid notions about "correctness" in language do not
realise this. They think language can be tied down by unchanging, unbending rules
about what is right and wrong.

wrong ✓ / *wright* ✗

Any language scholar will stress that this is not the case. Language reflects, and
adapts to, changing circumstances. Consider the jobs which develop a language of
their own. The different kinds of jargon used by policemen, lorry drivers, car
salesmen are all produced by the demands of the job. Within that particular situation
the language is effective.

List ten occupations which have particular jargons associated with them and give examples of their jargon.	
1.	6.
2.	7.
3.	8.
4.	9.
5.	10.

It is not just jobs which have special "languages" associated with them. Think of the words and phrases coined during the American Space Programme.

■
List five words or phrases associated with the Space Programme, e.g. "All systems go".
1.
2.
3.
4.
5.

Language is always affected by situation. In the Space Programme words and phrases were created to meet situations and events which were totally new. The basic job of language is to represent accurately what people see and hear about them.

■
Choose one of your particular interests or hobbies and write down some words and phrases associated with it, e.g. football — striker.

● | ADAPT YOUR LANGUAGE TO THE SITUATION |

You can only be versatile with language if you are sensitive to different situations.
You do not need to
develop a "split personality"
and change the way you
speak and write every few
minutes. But it is useful to
be aware of the way language can vary.

Here are the final words spoken as the first man landed on the Moon. Re-write them in what you consider is more "normal" English.

EAGLE	Pings, we got a good lock on. Altitude Light is out. Delta H is minus 2900.
CONTROL	Roger, we copy.
EAGLE	And the earth right out our front window — Houston, you're looking at our Delta H programme alarm.
CONTROL	That's affirmative Eagle Houston. We'll monitor your Delta H.
EAGLE	We're GO. Hang on tight. We're GO. Two thousand feet . . .
CONTROL	Eagle looking great. You're GO. We copy you down EAGLE.
EAGLE	Houston. Tranquility Base here. The Eagle has landed.

Neal Armstrong's language was hardly "correct" English, but it was effective in that situation.

 | THERE IS NO ONE CORRECT STYLE OF ENGLISH, ONLY EFFECTIVE ENGLISH

Bearing this in mind, what is effective English in a letter? It is not possible to give a final answer, because every letter and every situation is different. But it is possible to adopt a common-sense approach and ask questions about the words and phrases we use.

1. DOES THE EXPRESSION SHOW EVIDENCE OF CLEAR THINKING?

2. IS IT GENERALLY UNDERSTOOD?

3. IS IT NECESSARY TO THE MEANING?

If the answer to these questions is "Yes" then we can be reasonably confident that we are writing effectively.

> The Victorians had about twenty words to describe the different carriages pulled by horses. A late Victorian had only one phrase to describe a motor vehicle, "a horseless carriage". We have many words to describe different motor vehicles, but few to describe horse-drawn carriages. What does this tell you about language?

Consider the following opening sentences in letters of application. Comment on their effectiveness, or otherwise, in the light of the three questions discussed on the previous page.

1. I am writing to apply for the post of Clerical Assistant in your Forwarding Office.

2. With reference to your advertisement for a trainee hairdresser.

3. I have seen the advertisement in the paper and want the job.

4. I am in receipt of details about a vacancy as a laboratory technician with your company.

5. It is with much pleasure that I offer myself for the post of clerk-typist with your company.

6. Have you got any jobs vacant at your place?

7. I would respectfully submit myself for the appointment of trainee motor mechanic advertised in the "Gazette".

8. I would like to apply for the post of Trainee Salesman as advertised in "The Post" this week.

● MAKE A GOOD START TO A LETTER

The words we use, as well as the information we include, combine to produce the overall TONE of the letter. TONE refers to the amount of emphasis, and the kind of emphasis we put into our writing. The tone of a letter can indicate what sort of person the writer is. But we must realise that when people read what we write they may react to it in ways we do not anticipate. Many letters of application, even though they are written neatly and correctly, can give a poor impression of the writer. This is because of their TONE. Although they do not intend it, the writers create a poor impression of their personality. Perhaps the overall TONE of the letter makes the writer sound pompous and conceited. Perhaps he gives the impression of being self-centred, interested only in what a company can offer him, not what he can contribute to a company. It is obviously important that you check your letter for tone, as well as for more usual things, like spelling and punctuation. Ask yourself whether the overall impression you are giving is a good or bad one. Do you come across as eager or "half-soaked", purposeful or aimless, organised or chaotic.

Personality is important in life. Letters have a "personality" of their own, their TONE. It may well be the TONE of the letter which decides whether you are invited for an interview or not.

Of course the most off-putting impression that a letter can give is when it is presented carelessly.

■

Here are two paragraphs from a letter of application.
Basing your judgements on the tone of the extract, write
a description of the applicant's personality.

I have been looking around for the right job for sometime
now. It had to be one with good prospects and interesting
work. I was not prepared to do a dull and boring job.
Having seen your advertisement I decided that you might
be offering what I was after.

I have looked up your company in the Halchester Trade
Directory and am satisfied that you manufacture a
product which is in demand. You seem to be in a growing
market with prospects of expansion so I feel I could build
a real career with you.

■

Using the same information contained in the two
paragraphs of the previous exercise, re-write the extract
with what you consider is a more suitable tone

● USE AN APPROPRIATE TONE

Another problem we can create for ourselves, and our readers, is through the length of our sentences. Tests done in the United States of America have suggested the following surprising facts:—

1.   ONLY 4% OF READERS WILL UNDERSTAND A SENTENCE OF 27 WORDS

2.   75% WILL UNDERSTAND A SENTENCE OF 17 WORDS

3.   95% WILL UNDERSTAND A SENTENCE OF 8 WORDS

Additionally, of course, the longer the sentences you write, the more likely it is that you will make errors of punctuation and grammar.

Write down the grammatical definition of a sentence. Then break down sentence A into more sensible sentence units. You may re-phrase it.

Definition:

A   With reference to your advertisement for a shorthand typist advertised in last night's "Post" I would like to make an application for the post based on my C.S.E. qualifications and one year's full-time study at the Central Technical College on a Secretarial Course doing R.S.A. Shorthand and Typing plus English and an Introduction to Business Studies.

● | WATCH YOUR SENTENCE LENGTH |

But if some of the conventions about expressing ourselves need to be changed, some other letter writing conventions are very useful.

The second type of convention — the useful sort — is associated with the way a letter should be presented. The conventional lay-out of a letter presents the important information in a neat and attractive way. Employers expect you to know these conventions and use them. The example of a lay-out below is a good model for a letter of application.

1. Write your full address here and indent (i.e. slope) it.
   Write the date in full underneath.

2. Then write the name (or title) and address of the person you are writing to. This address is not indented.

3. Start the line with Dear Sir/Madam or the person's name if you know it.

4. Begin your first sentence below the salutation (Dear Sir etc.) and treat it as a paragraph — it should say which job you are applying for.

5. This is where the body of the letter goes — say something about yourself and why you feel qualified to do the job.

6. Final paragraph — indicate availability for interview etc.

7. Finish with "Yours faithfully", if you began with "Dear Sir/Madam" — finish with "Yours sincerely", if you used a name.

8. Sign your name clearly underneath.

Using the format on the previous page write a letter of application in answer to the following advertisement.

CLERICAL ASSISTANTS (2)

Possession of G.C.E. or C.S.E. Mathematics qualification desirable. Post-entry training facilities if required.
Apply to the Personnel Officer, Joseph Industries, Holly Lane, Midwich, M74 4LT.

1.

2.

3.

4.

5.

6.

7.

8.

● GET TO KNOW USEFUL CONVENTIONS

In addition to a letter, some employers like to receive further information about you in the form of a CURRICULUM VITAE. This is a brief outline of your life and career to date. The obvious advantage of enclosing a separate CURRICULUM VITAE is that it presents the important facts about you clearly. If you tried to pack them all into a letter the effect would be jumbled. You should not, however, just send a CURRICULUM VITAE when you apply for a job. You must always enclose a covering letter.

■

Fill in this example of a curriculum vitae with your own details.

Name

Address

Age   Date of Birth

Nationality   Marital Status

Education

Qualifications

Relevant Experience

Referees

● USE THE MOST SUITABLE METHOD OF COMMUNICATING

WRITING LETTERS

THINGS TO TRY

■ A   Write an essay on one of the following:—

The importance of "Good English"
Do you think the English Language is changing for
    the better?
How far do you believe that a child's language is
    influenced by his parents' abilities?

■ B   Draw up a check-list of points to help a friend
with his letter writing.

■ C   Write down some short extracts from broadcasts
by:—

1.   a disc jockey
2.   a sports commentator
3.   a newscaster

How does their language vary? Why does it?

■ D   List the points you think an employer needs to
know about you before he can decide whether
you might make a suitable employee.

■ E   A friend has asked you about setting out a
letter correctly. Write a letter to him explaining
the lay-out conventions and justify their use.

5. FILLING IN FORMS.

If the nineteenth century was in some ways a letter writing age the twentieth century could be called a form filling age. It seems today that you need to know how to fill in forms properly to survive. You need to fill in a form to drive a car or to ride a motor cycle. You need to fill in a form if you want a passport. Form filling comes into almost every aspect of daily life. Clearly it is an important skill to master. If you fill forms in carelessly giving wrong information or inaccurate facts, the consequences can be very troublesome.

■ Give some examples of forms which crop up in day-to-day living. List them in order of importance with explanations of their purpose. Suggest ways in which inaccurate facts could lead to trouble.

● GET YOUR FACTS RIGHT

It is highly probable that when you apply for a job you will have to fill in a fairly detailed form. A typical Job Application Form, broken down into two parts, can be found on the next two pages. Study it carefully, but do not fill it in yet.

53

APPLICATION FOR APPRENTICESHIP

Surname	Forenames

Address

Age	Date of Birth	Nationality

Father or Guardian's Name | His Occupation

Father or Guardian's Employer

EDUCATION SINCE AGE OF 11

School or College	Dates	Examinations taken (with results)

Give details of any impending examinations

Are you now at school or in employment? If in employment give details

SPARE TIME ACTIVITIES

Sports	Hobbies	Youth Organisations

HEALTH	Weight	Height	Chest Measurement	Have you any physical disabilities?

Are you related to anyone in the Company?   If so, state name and relationship

Date free to start

Give any additional information which may support this application

....
Signed — Applicant   Signed — Parent or Guardian

....
Date   Date

The form you have just studied poses problems. It is wrong to assume that forms can be filled in easily and with no trouble. They need attention and time.

First of all you need to read a form carefully. Quite often people misread forms and give the wrong information.

Use a dictionary to check the meaning of these words off the form on the previous two pages.

guardian

impending

hobbies

additional

STUDY FORMS BEFORE FILLING THEM IN

Once you are sure you understand every part of the form, you can begin to fill it in. It is a good idea to have some spare forms so that you can make one or two practice attempts. If you only have one copy of the form it will pay you to fill it in lightly with a pencil first. You can then rub out any mistakes and avoid crossings-out.

Boq Lane ~~Skool~~ ~~Skewl~~ Skule ~~Schewl~~

Remember that the form is a kind of ambassador for you. It speaks on your behalf. It should be as perfect as you can make it. This particularly applies to such basic things as neatness. It is always worth considering whether to print the form using BLOCK CAPITALS, or to write it. Sometimes you may print

Application for job as Slaughterhouse Assistant.

certain vital parts, for example your name and address, and write others.

CHARLS, Bucknam Pellis, LUNNON .

An untidy form can destroy your chances of an interview.

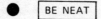 BE NEAT

You need to take care also with SPELLING and PUNCTUATION. The obvious way to check spelling is by using a dictionary. Punctuation is rather more difficult. The most common error which occurs on forms is to do with CAPITAL LETTERS. CAPITAL LETTERS should always be used with names, that is particular names of people, places and things.

> Here are some words and phrases which are similar to ones you may be using on application forms. Which require capital letters? Why?
>
> the evening mail (newspaper)
>
> central high school (school attended)
>
> football and squash (hobbies)
>
> 1st july
>
> certificate of secondary education
>
> british
>
> physics

TAKE CARE WITH SPELLING AND PUNCTUATION

FILLING IN FORMS

THINGS TO TRY

■ 1. Write a short essay on one of the following

(a) English spelling should be reformed.

(b) "We live in a society with too many clerks chasing too many forms."

(c) The importance of first impressions.

■ 2. Carefully fill in the forms on pages 53 and 54.

■ 3. Why do you think employers are so interested in applicants' leisure activities? How would you assess someone who said they had no hobbies at all?

■ 4. Study the form on pages 53 and 54 and suggest omissions and ways it might be improved.

■ 5. Design a form which you think does the job better.

THE SKILLS OF MAKING CONTACT

WHAT YOU HAVE LEARNED

CHAPTER 2 – READING FOR FACTS

- KNOWLEDGE COMES FROM READING

- YOU CAN ALWAYS EXTEND YOUR VOCABULARY

- TRY TO READ BETWEEN THE LINES

- MAKE NOTES TO REMEMBER FACTS

- LEARN IMPORTANT ABBREVIATIONS AND JARGON

CHAPTER 3 – SPEAKING ON THE TELEPHONE

- SPEAK CLEARLY

- WHEN DEALING WITH FACTS BE PRECISE

- BE POLITE

- LEARN TO OPERATE THE TELEPHONE

CHAPTER 4 – WRITING LETTERS

- WRITE NATURALLY, DON'T BE POMPOUS

- WRITE SIMPLY

- CHOOSE FAMILIAR WORDS WHENEVER POSSIBLE

THE SKILLS OF MAKING CONTACT

WHAT YOU HAVE LEARNED

CHAPTER 4 – WRITING LETTERS (CONTINUED)

- ADAPT YOUR LANGUAGE TO THE SITUATION

- THERE IS NO ONE CORRECT STYLE OF ENGLISH, ONLY EFFECTIVE ENGLISH

- MAKE A GOOD START TO A LETTER

- USE AN APPROPRIATE TONE

- WATCH YOUR SENTENCE LENGTH

- GET TO KNOW USEFUL CONVENTIONS

- USE THE MOST SUITABLE METHOD OF COMMUNICATING

CHAPTER 5 – FILLING IN FORMS

- GET YOUR FACTS RIGHT

- STUDY FORMS BEFORE FILLING THEM IN

- BE NEAT

- TAKE CARE WITH SPELLING AND PUNCTUATION

THE SKILLS OF MEETING PEOPLE

6. FIRST MEETING.

Most of your dealings with people are comparatively natural and easy. When you meet friends or relatives in familiar surroundings you have no reason to feel embarrassed or self-conscious. You accept people for what they are and assume that they do the same with you.

But we all know that there can be stress and worry when we meet new people, particularly if we meet them in unfamiliar surroundings.

■ Describe an embarrassing experience. Account for your embarrassment.

If you have made effective contact with a prospective employer then inevitably the company will invite you along. Almost certainly you will be given a formal interview, but before that you may be introduced to several people, and be encouraged to chat with them about the firm.

Meeting strangers on unfamiliar territory can be forbidding. It can be even more difficult when we want to impress people in order to get a job. This is to do with the way we communicate with each other.

We sometimes tend to assume that our speech is the most important means of communication. But this is only part of the story. In some ways, especially at a first meeting, speech is not the most important part of the communication process. Just think of what you notice when you meet someone new.

You notice things like:—

● CLOTHES

● HAIR

● FACIAL EXPRESSIONS

● EYES

● HANDS

All of these influence your opinion.

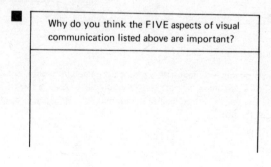

■

Why do you think the FIVE aspects of visual communication listed above are important?

What we see tells us a lot about people.

●  APPEARANCE IS IMPORTANT

Normally we use our facial expressions to support what we are saying. We say, "Thank you very much, I have enjoyed myself" and signal that we mean it in this way.

The words are heard but it is the expression, the NON-VERBAL sign, that really gets the message across. It is the smile that convinces, not the meaning of the words. People will usually believe the NON-VERBAL message, even if it is contradicted by the VERBAL message, i.e. the words. If we say, "I'm pleased to be here", but look like

THIS

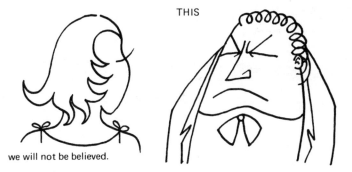

we will not be believed.

The eyes are particularly important in this process. They have often been called the "windows of the soul", meaning that they reveal our innermost, secret feelings. If you say something friendly, but your eyes reveal hostility, it is the eyes that will make the impact which counts.

When we try to remember people it is usually a visual image that we recall, not what they said to us. This image is particularly influenced by people's behaviour towards us, whether they were friendly or hostile, awkward or natural. One of the problems of meeting people for the first time is that we are not able to control completely the NON-VERBAL side of communication. You can choose your words carefully and tactfully, but your eyes can give you away.

If you are nervous and flustered your face may show it.

If you are only pretending to want a job your eyes may give you away.

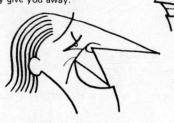

If you are superior and over-confident your expression will reveal it.

Draw caricature faces to match the following emotions.	
CONTEMPT	
AFFECTION	

OUR FACES SHOW OUR FEELINGS

What can we do to make sure that when we first meet people we create a good impression? There is no magic formula. But it may be useful to analyse carefully some of the devices that we all use to make contact with others.

When we meet people, before we even speak, the way we walk or stand has communicated to them. Our POSTURE, particularly the way we hold our head and shoulders, can give very definite messages about us.

POSTURE can reveal when we are lively and alert.

It can also show when we are dejected and depressed.

And it can show when we are angry and indignant.

There are no reliable ways of disguising your feelings so when you go to an important meeting, like seeking a job, try to be as calm and relaxed as possible.

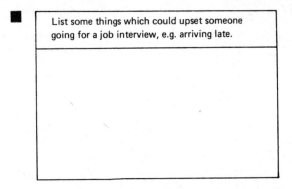

List some things which could upset someone going for a job interview, e.g. arriving late.

The body has a language all of its own. Good posture can help to make a positive first impression.

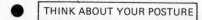 THINK ABOUT YOUR POSTURE

Another important mechanism of communication is the GAZE. When you are relaxing, talking to friends, you gaze at one another quite naturally. But in an unfamiliar situation, with new people, one of the things that most of us become a little self-conscious about is looking the other person "squarely in the eye". If we lack confidence, there is a great temptation to avoid looking at the other person completely. But if this is a temptation, it must be fought.

The GAZE is a very powerful method of communicating. If we virtually refuse to look at someone who is speaking to us, we can only create a very poor impression. By gazing at people  when we meet them, we are paying them the compliment of showing that we take notice of what they say. And we are being sensitive to them because by paying careful attention to their face we can respond to the emotions they display.

We can use our own facial expressions to help us create understanding and build a relationship. Nature makes sure that babies can smile before they can do practically anything else. This is a device for building up a warm relationship with the mother. A smile at the right time can be invaluable.

This does not mean, of course, that we should stare or smile fixedly at other people.

■
What might be the result of the following?
1. Staring persistently at a stranger.
2. Being introduced to someone and doing nothing but stare at him.
3. Being introduced to someone and refusing to look at him.

If you analyse yourself in a normal, friendly conversation you will find that you spend as much time looking away from your friend as you do looking at him. But by looking at him regularly from time to time you are reassuring him that you are still paying attention to what he says. You owe a new acquaintance the same politeness.

■

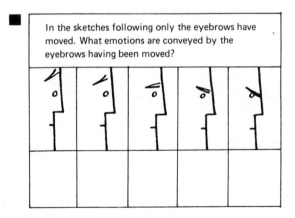

In the sketches following only the eyebrows have moved. What emotions are conveyed by the eyebrows having been moved?

● | BE ATTENTIVE TO PEOPLE

As well as POSTURE and GAZE we all use a third method of assisting language, we GESTURE with our hands. Different nationalities have different attitudes to gesturing. The Mediterranean peoples use GESTURE much more than we do in this country. Even so we have about twenty gestures in this country which nearly everyone understands without the aid of words.

> Describe three gestures which are generally understood and the situations in which you would expect them to be used.

In the situations you have described above, gesture may well have replaced words altogether. But generally, gestures aid and assist what we say. We deliberately use our hands to clarify or emphasise something we are saying. But like other kinds of NON-VERBAL communication, gestures can get out of control.

We can often decide not to express our feelings in words, but let them slip out through our gestures. Clenching fists can indicate tension. Tapping fingers may reveal anxiety. Too many gestures can distract your listener, and confuse him.

● | KEEP GESTURES UNDER CONTROL |

It should now be clear that NON-VERBAL communication will tell the truth about our inner feelings whether we like it or not. Actors are trained to use these non-verbal mechanisms to do their job. But it is not the aim of this book to help you play a part. The message is rather the opposite. If you are straightforward and sincere in your dealings with people you have nothing to fear. If when you apply for a job you are genuinely keen and enthusiastic then not only your words, but your WHOLE MANNER, will proclaim that loud and clear.

■
Imagine you have been asked for advice from a friend who has been invited on a preliminary tour of a factory where he wants to work. Add to the tips already on this list.

1. Be punctual

2. Take care with your appearance

If we consider carefully the theoretical material in this chapter it is possible to arrive at some practical guidelines for behaving appropriately when we meet people for the first time in a formal situation.

● PREPARE CAREFULLY AND
  BE PUNCTUAL

A GOOD APPEARANCE
AIDS CONFIDENCE   ●

● A FRIENDLY SMILE HELPS
  A CONVERSATION ALONG

BE CONSCIOUS OF   ●
YOUR POSTURE

● BE PREPARED TO LOOK PEOPLE
  "SQUARELY IN THE EYE"

USE APPROPRIATE GESTURES ●
(e.g. a firm handshake)
BUT DON'T OVERDO IT

● A POSITIVE ATTITUDE
  WILL HELP

FIRST MEETING

THINGS TO TRY

■ A Write an essay on any of the following:—

Fashion

Sign Language

The person I most admire

■ B Consider your own appearance, e.g. hair, style of dressing, etc. What immediate reactions do you think your appearance arouses in the following:—

a person of the same age and sex
a person of the same age but opposite sex
a parent of a friend
a teacher
an old age pensioner
a prospective employer

■ C Think about a close friend. Compare your present opinion of him/her with the way you responded to him/her at first meeting.

■ D List ten jobs where appearance is extremely important. Why is it?

■ E A friend has asked for your advice on methods of improving his posture. Provide him with some tips.

7. PREPARING FOR INTERVIEW.

We are all interviewed at one time or another. Interviews are used for many purposes besides that of simply getting a job. Outside work, interviews are used in a variety of situations,

by Bank Managers

by Committees of Clubs and Societies

by Building Society officials

Once at work interviews with people ranging from Trade Union officers to Managing Directors will affect our future. But to get into work, to achieve the future we really want, we must do well in the actual job selection interview.

Most people are afraid of interviews. This is partly to do with the dislike we all feel of being tested. A test implies the possibility of failure, and none of us likes to fail. For most jobs nowadays there will be several applicants, so that employers have to accept some and reject others. It is this possibility of rejection that most of us resent, and we must remember that the better the job the greater the competition, and therefore, the likelihood of disappointment.

But in addition to a fear of failure there is also, with many people, an ignorance of what interviews are really about. Because they do not understand the principles on which interviews are based they do not know how to cope with them.

This chapter will help you to prepare for interviews by increasing your understanding of what is involved in them.

■
> Why do you think employers need to interview people for jobs when they have all the relevant facts about them in letters and/or application forms?

Direct personal contact has many advantages over the written word. It is quicker and it allows for a greater understanding to develop between individuals. The personalities of the people involved become very important.

● PERSONALITY COUNTS AT INTERVIEW

We have already considered in the chapter "First Meeting" the way an impression of personality can be conveyed between people. This kind of communication is still vitally important in the formal interview.

But it is not just a general impression which will influence prospective employers. Nowadays interviewing techniques are highly developed. In some small companies jobs may still be secured on the basis of a foreman or manager "taking to you" at interview. Perhaps that kind of interview is no more than an informal chat and a conducted tour of the works. If that is what happens to you there will be a minimum of stress involved. But that is not usual.

It is much more likely that you will be interviewed in a formal way. That means in an appropriate room with an interviewer (or panel of interviewers) asking you carefully prepared questions. You will be one of several candidates for the job (or jobs) and your performance at interview will be compared with other people's. The whole interview will be organised with the idea of placing a little bit of stress on you.

This is because a prospective employer wants to see how you respond and behave under pressure.

■

What aspects of a formal interview can seem forbidding? Why?

● INTERVIEWS ARE STRESS SITUATIONS

It is important therefore to try to remain as cool as possible under pressure. Remember how revealing posture can be. Keep control of your hands and arms, relax your shoulders and don't lose control.

Interviewers usually remain calm and methodical. Most of them use some kind of INTERVIEW PLAN to help them reach as objective and unbiased a decision as possible. An interview plan enables an interviewer to assess candidates against the desired requirements for a job. One of the best known plans is called the Seven Point Plan, designed by the National Institute of Industrial Psychology. For this plan an interviewer has to assess candidates in seven categories.

● PHYSICAL CHARACTERISTICS

● ATTAINMENTS

● INTELLIGENCE

● SPECIAL APTITUDES

● INTERESTS

● DISPOSITION

● CIRCUMSTANCES

Using these seven categories employers can create what is called a JOB SPECIFICA-
TION. This is a detailed analysis of the requirements of a particular job. An example
of a JOB SPECIFICATION begins on this page and continues on the next.

JOB SPECIFICATION FOR THE POST OF CLERK-TYPIST IN THE GENERAL OFFICE

REQUIREMENTS

1.   Physical

     Position suitable for a man or woman
     Age sixteen to eighteen preferred
     Disabled person could be employed, provided disability does not greatly
     interfere with mobility
     Good speech and manner required for telephone duties
     Appearance important, neat and tidy
     Health to be good enough to avoid frequent absence
     Build not relevant
     Eyesight normal, spectacles not relevant
     Hearing good, particularly for telephone duties

2.   Attainments

     Education — good general education, with G.C.E., C.S.E. grade 1 or R.S.A.
     stage II pass in English, and preferably with some evidence of ability in
     arithmetic
     Vocational training — R.S.A. stage II Typewriting and Office Practice
     Should be able to operate a switchboard and normal office machinery

3.   Intelligence

     High intelligence not needed, as promotion prospects limited, but should be
     sufficiently alert and intelligent to work without constant supervision and to
     use initiative.

4.   Special Aptitudes

   Aptitudes associated with good clerical work:

         Methodical approach
         Neat handwriting and figures
         Attention to detail
         English and arithmetic at reasonable standard

5.   Interests

   Needs to work as member of team so hobbies involving teams, clubs, etc. might be an advantage.

6.   Disposition

   Reliable and conscientious attitude to work
   Helpful and considerate towards colleagues and telephone callers
   Willingness to be trained, and to attend a further education course, if necessary.

7.   Circumstances

   Preferably available to work normal day from 9 to 5.30, though a married woman with school age children willing to work from 9.30 to 4 could be considered (this would mean re-arranging the postal duties).

With a Job Specification as a guide an interviewer has a very clear idea of the kind of person who would suit the job. The questions he asks will probably be tailored around the requirements specified. If we are familiar with the techniques involved in Interview Plans and Job Specifications it can help us see into the minds of the interviewers and anticipate their questions.

Write a Job Specification for the kind of job you
want, using the Clerk-Typist example as a model.
How do you think you measure up to it?

Physical Requirements

Attainments

Intelligence

Special Aptitudes

Interests

Disposition

Circumstances

Clearly when we go for interview the people who are going to ask us questions are going to be thoroughly prepared.

● │ INTERVIEWS CAN BE SEARCHING │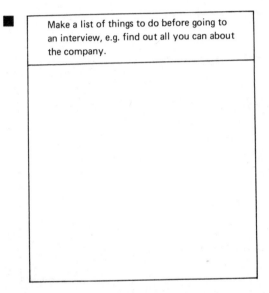

The least we can do is to prepare as well.

■ | Make a list of things to do before going to an interview, e.g. find out all you can about the company.

It is important that you see the interview as a TWO-WAY process. It is a mistake to regard your role as merely passive. One way to help you play a positive role is to anticipate some of the questions and consider possible answers.

In normal conversation you very rarely have to answer questions, apart from giving opinions. In interview you are going to have to give factual answers to a whole series of questions. Some candidates "dry up" under this pressure. The right sort of anticipation will help you avoid this.

82

You are an employer selecting people for the kind
of job you want. Provide two searching questions
for each of the categories in the Seven Point Plan.
Avoid questions which can be answered with a
simple "Yes" or "No". For example "Are you
reliable?"

PHYSICAL REQUIREMENTS

ATTAINMENTS

INTELLIGENCE

SPECIAL APTITUDES

INTERESTS

DISPOSITION

CIRCUMSTANCES

Having written out the questions now consider how
you, as an applicant, would go about answering
them.

This is also an appropriate time to consider what you can ask at the end of an
interview when you are invited to put questions. One obvious example is "What are
the future prospects?"

List some questions which might usefully be asked by applicants at the conclusion of an interview.

● DO YOUR HOMEWORK

Now write in your answers to these common interview questions.

Which were your favourite subjects at school?

Why?

What hobbies do you have?

Why do you enjoy them?

Why do you want to work for this particular company?

What attracts you to the job?

What do you think you can offer the company?

Remember, however, that there are dangers in rehearsing answers to questions. It would be very foolish to attend an interview with the intention of repeating prepared answers, parrot-fashion. On the contrary, it is essential that you listen carefully and answer the question put to you. What careful preparation can do is to clarify your own thoughts and ideas about yourself and the job so that you answer questions more effectively.

> Consider your intended job and why you think you are suited to it. List those qualities which strengthen your claim to the job. Then list your "weak" qualities.

Remember, the applicant's role at interview is not passive. Almost certainly you will have special qualities or knowledge which will impress an employer. Make sure you know where your strengths lie and that you mention them in the interview.

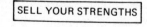 SELL YOUR STRENGTHS

PREPARING FOR INTERVIEW

THINGS TO TRY

■ A   Write an essay on any of the following

"Honesty is the best policy"

"The right attitudes?"

Leisure

■ B   Invent your own Interview Plan

■ C   Write a detailed description of yourself to give as vivid a picture as possible to someone who has never seen you.

■ D   Find out all you can about the work of Personnel Departments in large companies. Write a description of the work of a Personnel Officer.

■ E   Consider the seven categories in the Seven Point Interview Plan. List them in order of importance and priority, assuming you were interviewing candidates for a job. Account for your decisions.

8. ATTENDING FOR INTERVIEW.

It is now time to consider the most crucial part of the whole process of "Getting a Job", the actual interview. From the moment you walk into the interview room (probably with your nerves jangling) until the moment you leave, you are under scrutiny.

Many of the factors we have discussed in "First Meeting" operate NOW, your appearance, your posture and so on. But let's concentrate on practical things in this section. The first practical problems you face are what to say, and what to do, after entering the room.

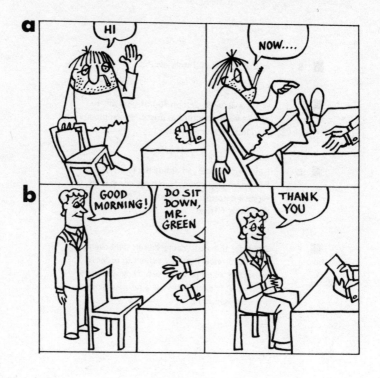

In the strip cartoons on the previous page which candidate created the more favourable impression? Why? How would you enter an interview room?

FIRST IMPRESSIONS COUNT

Once you are seated in the interview room, sit in a comfortable position and don't fidget. Remember the way you sit can be offputting.

What impressions do you get from the way the following people are sitting?

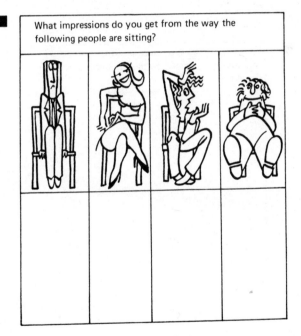

THE BODY HAS A LANGUAGE OF ITS OWN

Once the questions begin, you need to listen carefully and give good answers. Pay attention to delivery. The way you speak is almost as important as what you say. There is often a temptation to murmur and speak quietly when you are nervous. That is a trap to avoid, so without shouting,

● SPEAK UP

Employers will learn little about you if you answer questions with just a "Yes" or a "No". Try to give full answers, but avoid going on and on. Be prepared to explain why you like certain things and why you have come to certain decisions. Don't get irritated if you are not understood at once. Your TONE of voice will soon reveal your emotions and if you are resentful of the interviewers they will sense it.

■ List some things you notice about the way people speak, e.g. accent. Indicate how they influence your attitude to people.

● ANSWER CLEARLY

If you are being interviewed by several people it is sometimes difficult to know where to look when you are giving answers.

EYE CONTACT between people is very important. The way to hold the attention of several listeners is to make eye contact with each of them briefly.

$$X + Y^2 + Z$$
$$-h^3 \div Q + [x+y]^2$$
$$=$$

Experts estimate that the average length of an eye contact is six seconds. If you glance at each member of the interviewing panel in turn you will be including all of the panel in your answers, and thereby make them more interested in you.

It is generally agreed that eye contact is in itself a means of communication. What do you think you can tell about someone from simply looking into his eyes?

TRY TO HOLD THE INTERVIEWERS' INTEREST

And so finally we come to the end of the interview. All your forethought and preparation have been brought to bear in the interview room. Now one of three things can happen.

You may be offered the job.

You may be told that a decision will be made later and the company will let you know whether you have been successful in a few days' time.

Or you may be told that the company are not prepared to offer you the job, for a variety of reasons.

Let's consider the first possibility. If you are offered a job be sure that you want it before you accept it. It is possible to accept a job and then later change your mind, but that is not very desirable. It inconveniences the employer, and does your reputation harm. If you have some doubts, ask further questions to try and set your mind at rest. If you still have doubts, ask whether you can have some time to think the matter over. Most employers appreciate the importance of the decision you are making and will allow you time to deliberate.

Once you have decided to accept, don't listen to people who say, "You have made a mistake", or "That company is no good." If you like the job you have got, if you are keen and enthusiastic about it, then you could have no better starting point for a career.

If you are not given a definite decision on the day of the interview, you may have, what seems to you, a very long wait to hear whether you have got the job or not. You may be tempted to get in touch with the firm to enquire. This is not generally a good idea. You may make a nuisance of yourself, which is not going to help if you are a "borderline" candidate for the job. You may just convince someone that you are too much of a nuisance to employ. You can only wait patiently.

But what if the worst happens? What if, after all your preparation, you are turned down for the job?

That is where our final chapter comes in.

ATTENDING FOR INTERVIEW

THINGS TO TRY

■ A   Write an essay on any of the following:—

Should more time be given in schools to careers advice?

Decisions

Problems of unemployment

■ B   Organise some mock-up interviews with your class mates or colleagues. Assess one another's performance.

■ C   What would you consider a fair wage/salary for the following?

a school leaver aged 16

a college leaver aged 18

an engineering apprentice "coming out of his time"

How do you judge "fair"?

■ D   What social facilities would you look for in a company? How important would they be to you?

■ E   What language uses do you find moving? Analyse an example, poem, song, speech, etc. to try and explain its power.

THE SKILLS OF MEETING PEOPLE

WHAT YOU HAVE LEARNED

CHAPTER 6 — FIRST MEETING

- APPEARANCE IS IMPORTANT
- OUR FACES SHOW OUR FEELINGS
- THINK ABOUT YOUR POSTURE
- BE ATTENTIVE TO PEOPLE
- KEEP GESTURES UNDER CONTROL

CHAPTER 7 — PREPARING FOR INTERVIEW

- PERSONALITY COUNTS AT INTERVIEW
- INTERVIEWS ARE STRESS SITUATIONS
- INTERVIEWS CAN BE SEARCHING
- DO YOUR HOMEWORK
- SELL YOUR STRENGTHS

CHAPTER 8 — ATTENDING FOR INTERVIEW

- FIRST IMPRESSIONS COUNT
- THE BODY HAS A LANGUAGE OF ITS OWN
- SPEAK UP
- ANSWER CLEARLY
- TRY TO HOLD THE INTERVIEWERS' INTEREST

THE SKILLS OF
SELF - APPRAISAL

9. ASSESS YOUR PERFORMANCE.

This short section is basically a check-list to help you learn from experience. It is almost impossible to go through life without some disappointment over jobs. You cannot expect to get every job you apply for. If you do, you may not be stretching yourself sufficiently or aiming high enough.

Suppose now that you have applied for a job and failed at some stage. What can be learned from this failure? Let us take it stage by stage.

1.   WAS THE JOB RIGHT FOR YOU?

        Did you consider your own temperament and abilities in relation to the job before applying?
        Were you genuinely keen and enthusiastic about it?

2.   DID THE JOB TURN OUT TO BE DIFFERENT FROM YOUR EXPECTATIONS?

        Did you read the advertisements carefully?
        Did you attempt to find out more about the job and the firm?

3.   DID YOU MAKE CONTACT WITH THE FIRM SUCCESSFULLY?

        If you had to use the telephone did you use it properly?
        Are you satisfied you gave enough attention to any letters or forms involved?
        Was the standard of your written English good enough?
        Did you give enough time and effort to your letter and/or form?

4.   DID YOU COPE WITH MEETING NEW PEOPLE?

        Did you take care with your appearance?
        Were you friendly and natural?
        Did you have a positive attitude?

5.   DID YOU PREPARE FOR THE INTERVIEW?

Were you informed about the company?
Did you know what the job involved?
Were you able to anticipate some questions?
Were you punctual?

6.   WERE YOU SATISFIED WITH YOUR INTERVIEW PERFORMANCE?

Did you emphasise what you intended?
Did you speak up?
Did you make your answers as interesting as possible?

Wherever you have answered NO on this list of questions, you have identified a problem area. Consider where you have failed and learn from it. Failure never matters if we use it to build success.

Next time you can put right your mistakes.

● AND THERE USUALLY IS A NEXT TIME ●

GETTING A JOB

Some practical tips

DO	DON'T
THINK CAREFULLY ABOUT CHOOSING A JOB	BE CASUAL ABOUT JOB SEEKING
USE ALL THE HELP AND ADVICE YOU CAN GET	APPLY FOR ANY JOB
CONSULT ALL THE RELEVANT SOURCES FOR JOBS	CONFINE YOUR APPLICATIONS TO ONE COMPANY
APPLY WIDELY	GET DISAPPOINTED AND DOWNHEARTED IF YOU FAIL
WRITE DOWN AS MANY INTERVIEW QUESTIONS AS YOU CAN REMEMBER AFTER BEING INTERVIEWED	BE PUT OFF BY PESSIMISTS
LOOK AT THEM BEFORE YOU GO TO YOUR NEXT INTERVIEW	GIVE UP